EASIEST 5-FIN
PIANO COLLEC

CH00330346

Adele

**15 hit Adele songs
arranged for 5-finger piano**

Wise Publications
part of The Music Sales Group
London / New York / Paris / Sydney / Copenhagen / Berlin / Madrid / Tokyo

SOMEONE LIKE YOU

Words & Music by Adele Adkins & Daniel Wilson

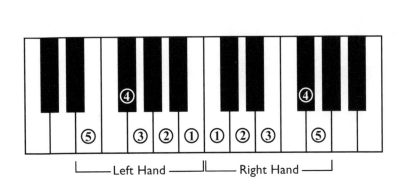

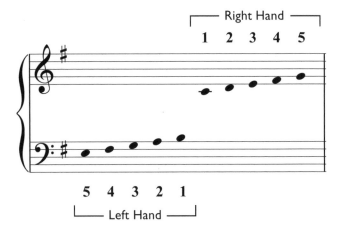

Nev - er mind,___ I'll find some - one like

you.___ I wish noth - ing but___ the

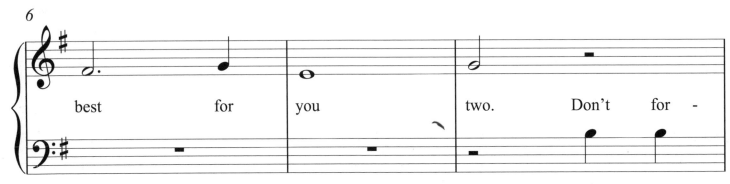

best for you two. Don't for -

HOMETOWN GLORY

Words & Music by Adele Adkins

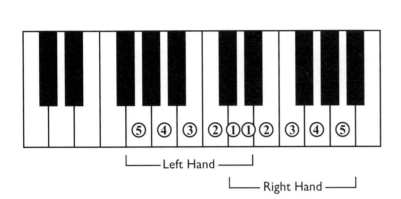

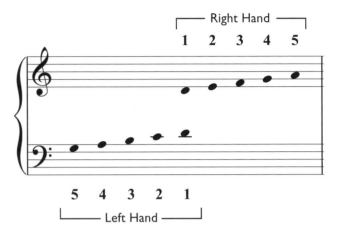

Longingly ♩ = 108

Round my home - town, mem -

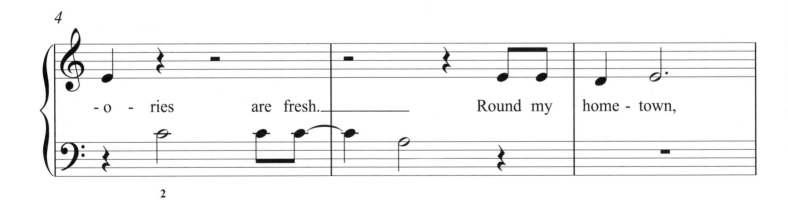

-o - ries are fresh. Round my home - town,

oh, the peo - ple I've met are the

won - ders of my___ world, are the won - ders of my___

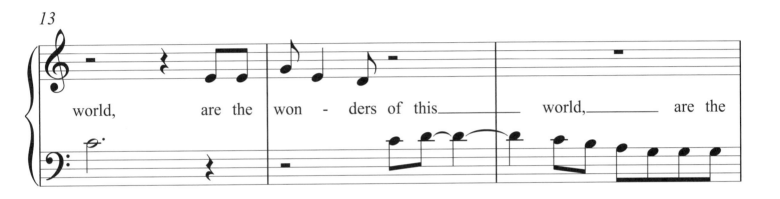

world, are the won - ders of this___ world,___ are the

won - ders___ of___ my world,___ of___ my

world,___ yeah,___ of___ my world.

CHASING PAVEMENTS

Words & Music by Adele Adkins & Eg White

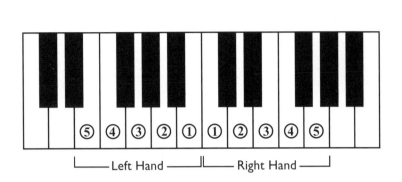

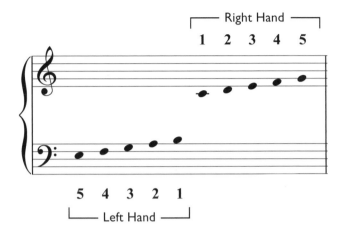

Expressively and steadily ♩ = 80

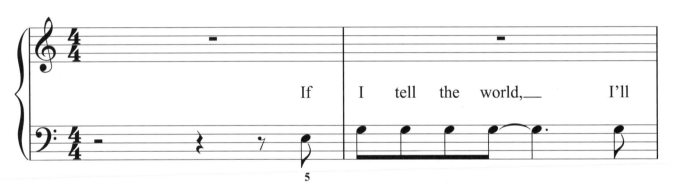

If I tell the world,___ I'll

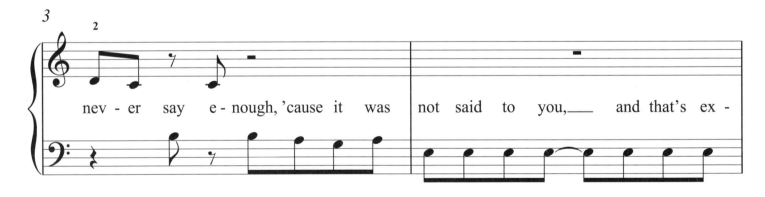

nev - er say e - nough, 'cause it was not said to you,___ and that's ex -

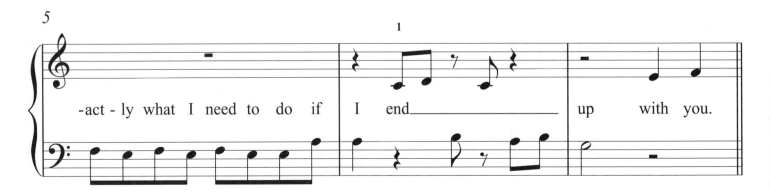

-act - ly what I need to do if I end_____ up with you.

MAKE YOU FEEL MY LOVE

Words & Music by Bob Dylan

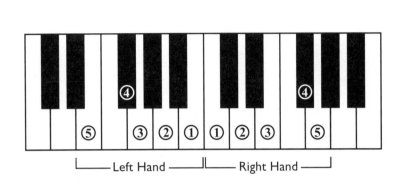

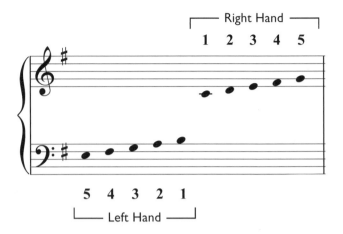

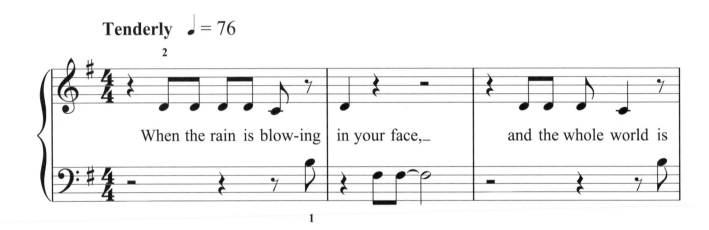

When the rain is blow-ing in your face,— and the whole world is

on your case,— I could of-fer you a warm em-brace—

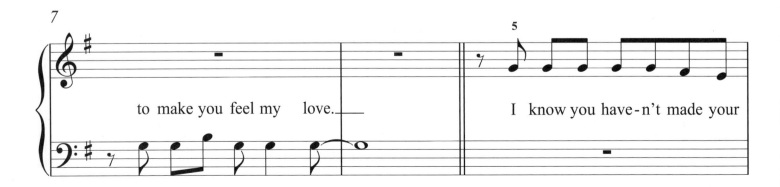

to make you feel my love.— I know you have-n't made your

SET FIRE TO THE RAIN

Words & Music by Fraser Smith & Adele Adkins

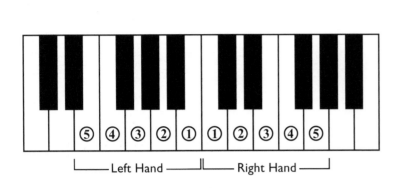

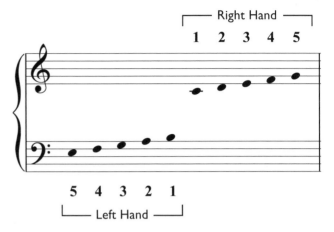

Powerfully ♩ = 108

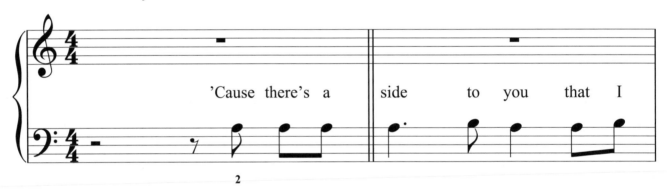

'Cause there's a side to you that I

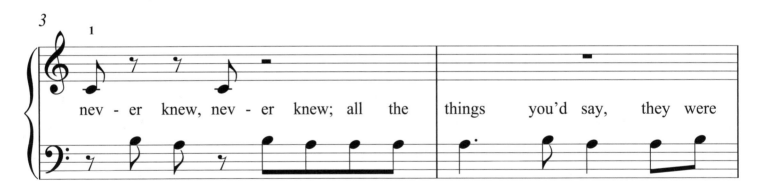

nev - er knew, nev - er knew; all the things you'd say, they were

nev - er true, nev - er true. And the games you'd play you would

TURNING TABLES

Words & Music by Ryan Tedder & Adele Adkins

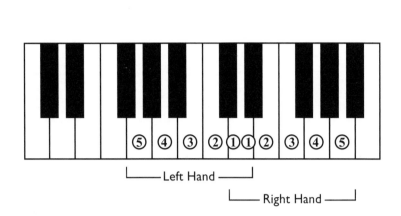

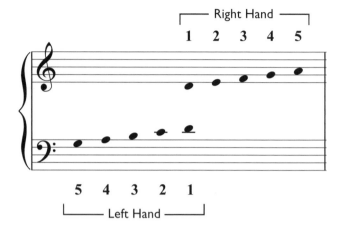

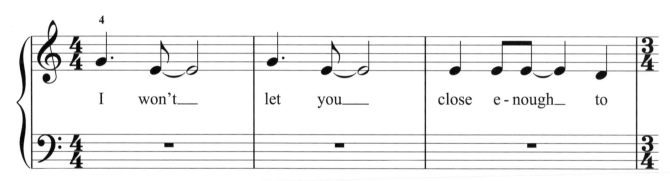

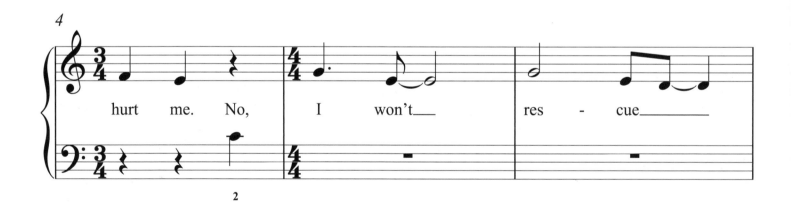

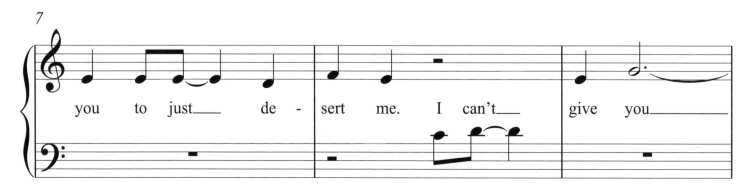

MELT MY HEART TO STONE

Words & Music by Francis White & Adele Adkins

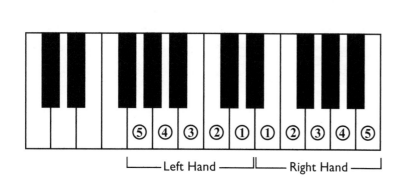

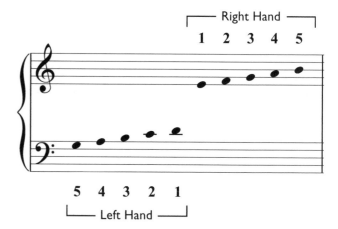

Tenderly ♩ = 82

Right under my feet is air made of

bricks that pulls me down and turns me weak for you. I find my-self re-

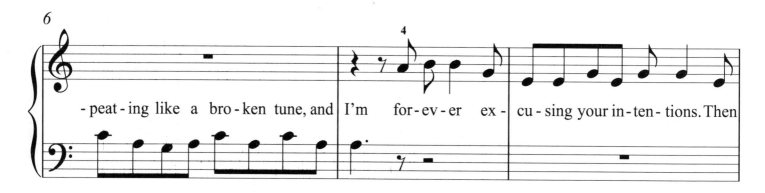

-peat-ing like a bro-ken tune, and I'm for-ev-er ex-cu-sing your in-ten-tions. Then

ONE AND ONLY

Words & Music by Greg Wells, Daniel Wilson & Adele Adkins

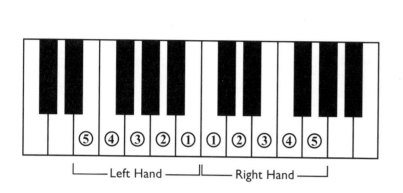

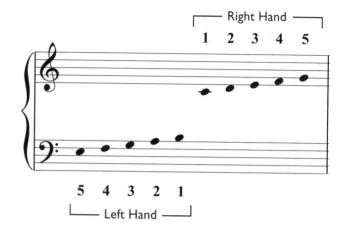

Smoothly ♩ = 132

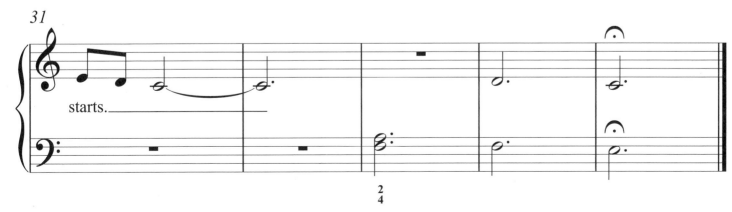

COLD SHOULDER

Words & Music by Adele Adkins

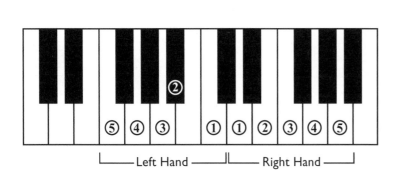

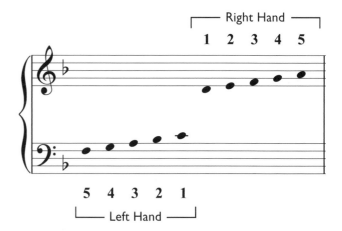

Rhythmically ♩ = 100

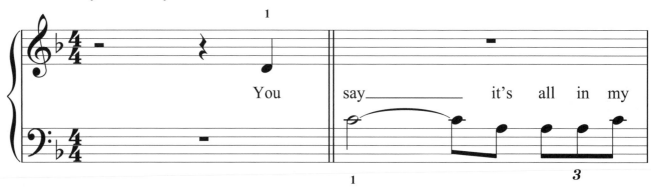

You say_____ it's all in my

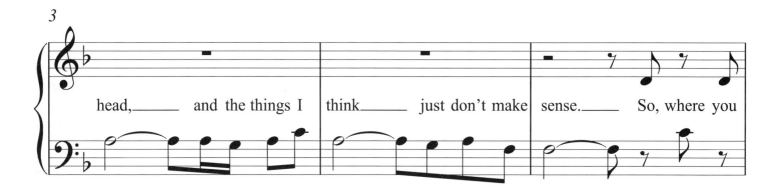

head,_____ and the things I think_____ just don't make sense._____ So, where you

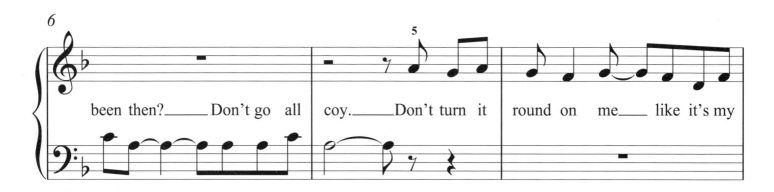

been then?_____Don't go all coy._____Don't turn it round on me_____ like it's my

RIGHT AS RAIN

Words & Music by J Silverman, Adele Adkins & Leon Michels

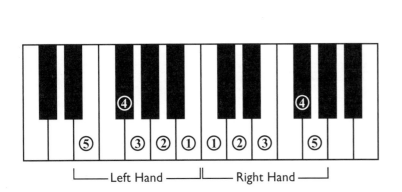
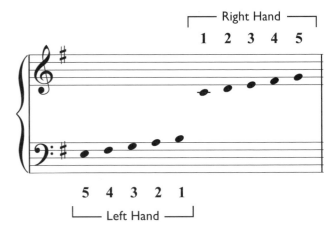

Energetically ♩ = 116

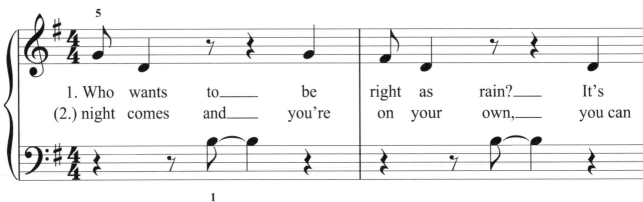

1. Who wants to___ be right as rain?___ It's
(2.) night comes and___ you're on your own,___ you can

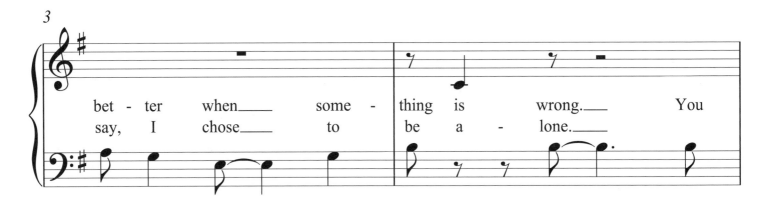

bet - ter when___ some - thing is wrong.___ You
say, I chose___ to be a - lone.___

get ex - cite - ment in your bones,___ and ev - 'ry - thing___ you
Who wants to___ be right as rain?___ It's

DAYDREAMER

Words & Music by Adele Adkins

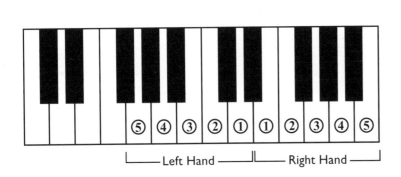

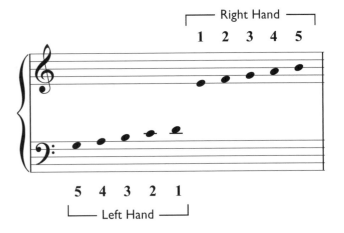

Day - dream - er,___ with eyes that make you

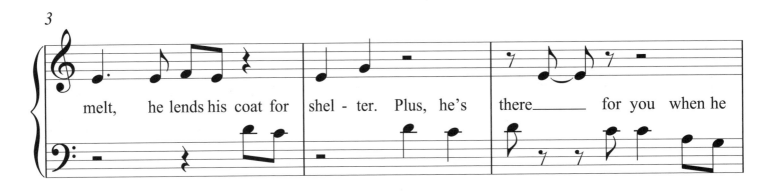

melt, he lends his coat for shel - ter. Plus, he's there___ for you when he

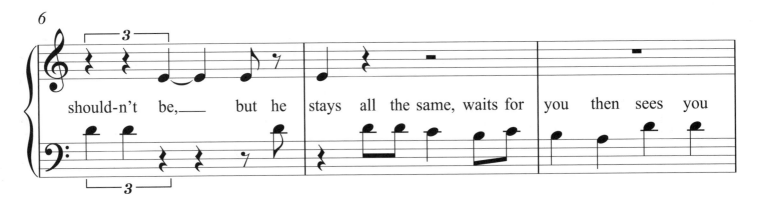

should-n't be,___ but he stays all the same, waits for you then sees you

TIRED

Words & Music by Francis White & Adele Adkins

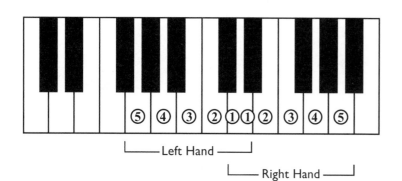

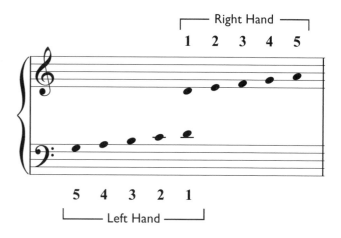

Simply ♩ = 96

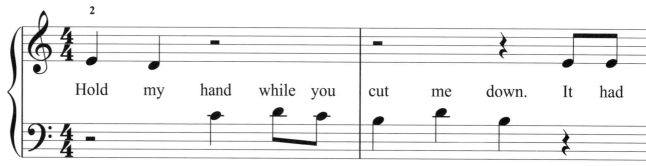

Hold my hand while you cut me down. It had

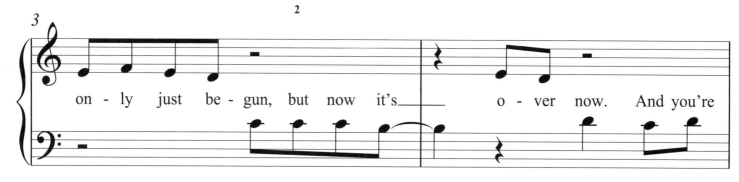

on - ly just be - gun, but now it's o - ver now. And you're

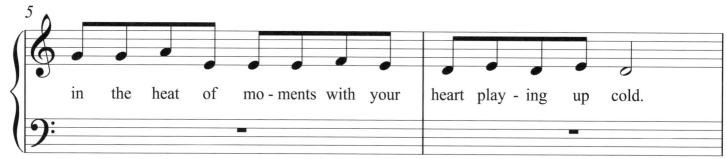

in the heat of mo - ments with your heart play - ing up cold.

I'm be - tween the mid - dle watch - ing has - ti - ness un - fold. On

I'LL BE WAITING

Words & Music by Adele Adkins & Paul Epworth

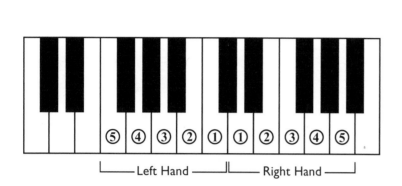

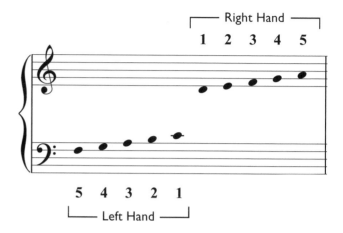

Energetically ♩ = 138

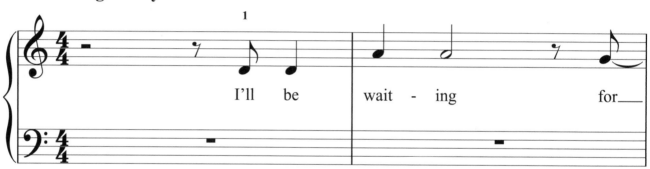

I'll   be   wait - ing   for___

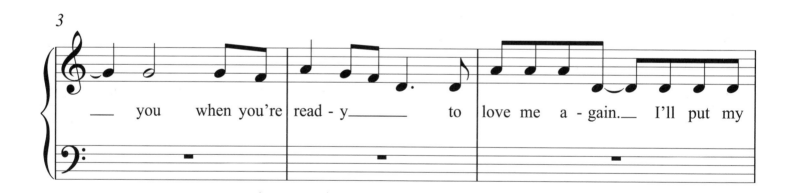

___ you   when you're   read - y_____   to   love me a - gain.___   I'll put my

hands   up,   I'll___   do   ev - 'ry-thing diff - 'rent, I'll be

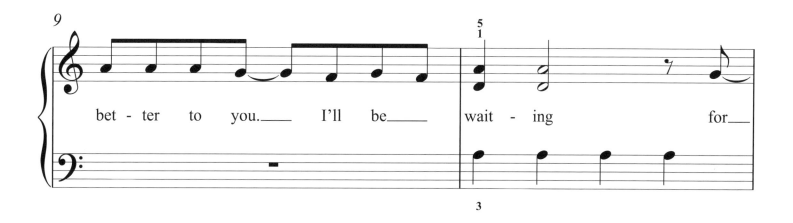

bet - ter to you.___ I'll be___ wait - ing for___

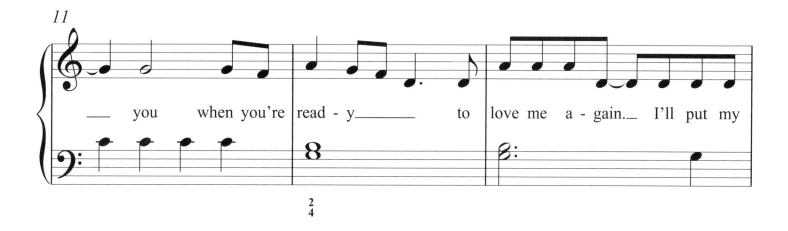

___ you when you're read - y___ to love me a - gain.___ I'll put my

hands up, I'll___ be

some-bod - y diff - 'rent, I'll be bet - ter to you.___

ROLLING IN THE DEEP

Words & Music by Adele Adkins & Paul Epworth

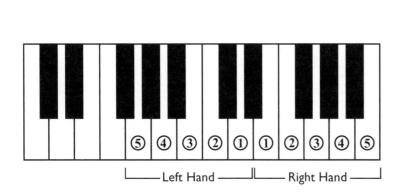

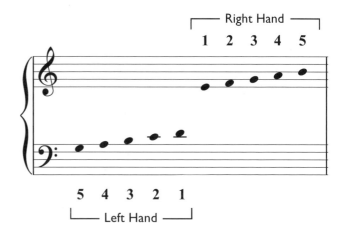

Rhythmically, with confidence ♩ = 100

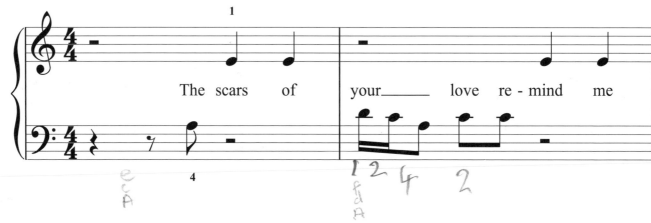

The scars of your_____ love re-mind me

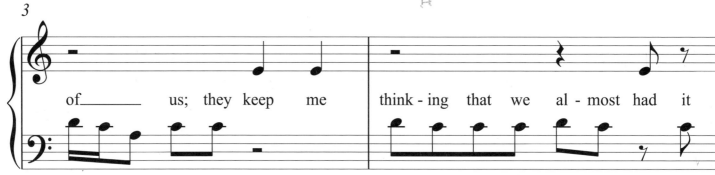

of_____ us; they keep me think-ing that we al-most had it

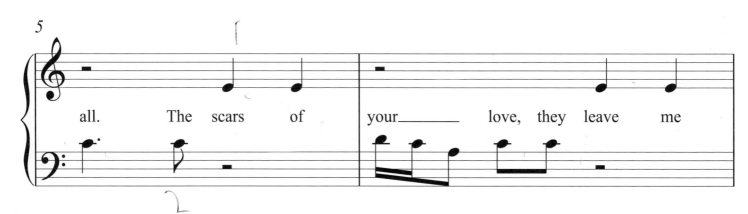

all. The scars of your_____ love, they leave me

CRAZY FOR YOU

Words & Music by Adele Adkins

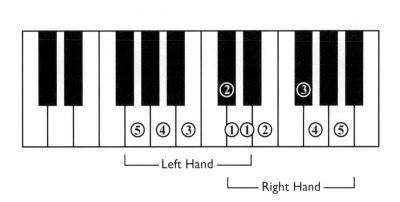

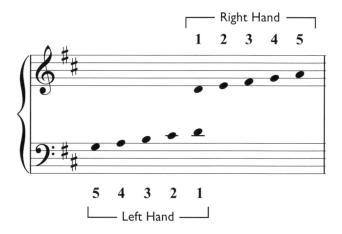

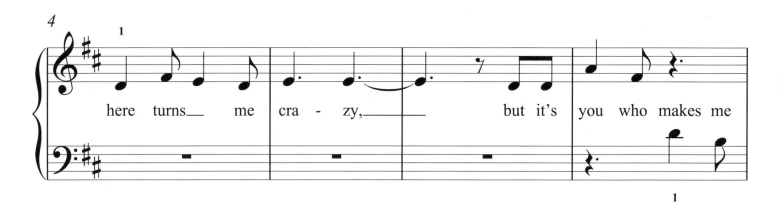

EASIEST 5-FINGER PIANO COLLECTION

ALSO AVAILABLE IN THE SERIES...

Abba
A great collection of 15 classic Abba hits, including 'Dancing Queen', 'Fernando', 'Take A Chance On Me' and 'Thank You For The Music'.
AM998404

Ballads
A superb collection of 15 well-known ballads, including 'Fix You', 'I Have A Dream', 'Let It Be' and 'What A Wonderful World'.
AM995346

The Beatles
15 classic Beatles hits including 'All My Loving', 'Hey Jude', 'She Loves You' and 'Yellow Submarine'.
NO91322

New Chart Hits
15 top chart hits including 'Cry Me Out', 'Don't Stop Believin'', 'Issues', 'Just Dance' and 'Russian Roulette'.
AM1001077

Classical Favourites
15 classical pieces including 'Jupiter' (Holst), 'Lullaby' (Brahms), 'Minuet In G' (J.S. Bach) and 'Spring' (Vivaldi).
AM998393

Film Songs
15 great film songs including 'Breaking Free', 'Don't Worry, Be Happy', 'Somewhere Out There' and 'You've Got A Friend In Me'.
AM995335

Showtunes
15 great showtunes including 'Any Dream Will Do', 'Circle Of Life', 'Mamma Mia' and 'My Favourite Things'.
AM995324

Today's Hits
15 of today's current chart hits including 'Hallelujah', 'Human', 'If I Were A Boy' and 'Viva La Vida'.
AM998415

...PLUS MANY MORE

Download to your computer a set of piano accompaniments for this *Adele* edition (to be played by a teacher/parent).
Visit: **www.hybridpublications.com**
Registration is free and easy.
Your registration code is YU417

Published by
Wise Publications
14-15 Berners Street,
London W1T 3LJ, UK.

Exclusive Distributors:
Music Sales Limited
Distribution Centre, Newmarket Road,
Bury St Edmunds, Suffolk IP33 3YB, UK.
Music Sales Pty Limited
20 Resolution Drive, Caringbah,
NSW 2229, Australia.

Order No. AM1004498
ISBN 978-1-78038-476-4
This book © Copyright 2011 Wise Publications,
a division of Music Sales Limited.

Edited by Jenni Norey.
Arranged by Chris Hussey.
Music processed by Camden Music Services.

Printed in the EU.

Your Guarantee of Quality
As publishers, we strive to produce every book to the highest commercial standards. This book has been carefully designed to minimise awkward page turns and to make playing from it a real pleasure. Particular care has been given to specifying acid-free, neutral-sized paper made from pulps which have not been elemental chlorine bleached. This pulp is from farmed sustainable forests and was produced with special regard for the environment. Throughout, the printing and binding have been planned to ensure a sturdy, attractive publication which should give years of enjoyment. If your copy fails to meet our high standards, please inform us and we will gladly replace it.

www.musicsales.com